COVID-19

A PHYSICIAN'S TAKE ON THE EXAGGERATED FEAR OF THE CORONAVIRUS

3RD EDITION

$9.99

COVID-19

A PHYSICIAN'S TAKE ON THE EXAGGERATED FEAR OF THE CORONAVIRUS

3RD EDITION

Jeffrey I. Barke, M.D.

THE AMERICAS GROUP

The Americas Group
520 S. Sepulveda Blvd., Suite 204
Los Angeles, California 90049-3534 U.S.A.

ISBN
978-0-935047-96-7

Description: Second edition. | Los Angeles, CA : The Americas Group, 2020. | Includes index. | Summary: "This book of brief essays methodically examines the major Covid-19 issues to determine what is fact and what is myth. It is written by a family physician who pointedly differs on the threat posed by Covid-19 to the American people, then challenges current conventional wisdom on what should be done about the schools, the economy and public activity with reason, honesty and scientific findings."— Provided by publisher.

Printed in India by
AEGEAN OFFSET PRINTING, LTD.

CONTENTS

FOREWORD

 THE TALMUD, JU-
DAISM'S second
holiest work
after the Bible,
a repository of
law, folklore
and wisdom
the size of an
encyclopedia, contains an amaz-
ing statement: "The best physicians go to hell."

Now, why would a holy
work say such a thing about physicians, those who are arguably

engaged in the holiest work of all—saving human lives? Moreover, why would it say such a thing about "the best" of them?

The answer is the ancient rabbis understood how tempting it can be for a physician, more than for the members of other professions, to think of himself —and for others to think of him — as a god.

I can say with certainty that the Talmudic principle does not apply to Dr. Jeffrey Barke. He is certainly one of the best physicians, but he knows that no doctor, not even those who run the CDC or the FDA or who edit the *New England Journal of Medicine* or *The Lancet*, is a god. That is why he is prepared to challenge conventional medical wisdom when doing so is warranted by the facts.

He has taken a hard look at the lockdowns implemented in America and in almost every other country at the behest of doctors in response to the novel coronavirus known as Covid-19, and he sees a mistake the likes of which no one alive at this time has seen.

Unlike most of his colleagues, he not only sees the price people pay because of the virus, he sees the price paid because of the lockdown: the impoverishment of hundreds of millions of people around the world, the impoverishment and near-impoverishment of countless Americans, the increase in depression, suicide, children's loss of education, family tension, increased drug use, recovering addicts returning to their addiction, people delaying or forgoing necessary medical treatments and much more. And he sees the political turmoil that inactivity, economic depression and loss of income inevitably lead to.

Also, unlike many of his colleagues, he has the courage to advocate medical treatments that work, irrespective of what the medical establishment has pronounced, not because of science, but because of politics.

The combination of medical expertise, courage, and wisdom is very rare. We have all three traits in Jeffrey Barke. That's why he needs to be heard.

And that's why I think the ancient rabbis would have said, "Here's one physician who will go to Heaven."

I certainly think so.

Dennis Prager
Radio talk show host,
lecturer and author
whose intellect and integrity
have influenced millions of
lives

INTRODUCTION

THERE ARE MANY great traditions in American political life. Freedom of speech is perhaps the most fundamental. That freedom not only permits the widest possible expression of views but encourages dissent no matter how broadly or how firmly the majority view is held.

Dealing with Covid-19 is one of those subjects that is stimulating continuing controversy. This second edition of *A Physician's Take on the Exaggerated Fear of the Coronavirus* allows Dr. Barke to expand his thinking on many of the topics covered in the first edition.

Just as the four physicians who signed the American Declaration of Independence pledged their lives, their fortunes and their sacred honor to renounce the rule of King George III in the American colonies, so Dr. Barke, a family physician in Newport Beach, California, differs with the conventional wisdom concerning the threat of Covid-19 to the American population.

In the essays on the following pages, Dr. Barke examines the major Covid-19 issues to determine what is fact and what is myth. He buttresses his analyses with reason, honesty and scientific findings that go against much of what the public has been led to believe from government officials and the media.

Readers are urged to examine for themselves whether his ideas make sense. Keep an open mind. Be part of that other great American tradition that believes in unbridled and fair debate to arrive at new conclusions. Remember the words of George Bernard Shaw: "Those who cannot change their minds, cannot change anything."

Godfrey Harris
Public policy consultant
and managing editor of
The Americas Group

FIRST, DO NO HARM —
PRIMUM NON NOCERE

HIPPOCRATES WAS A Greek physician who lived some 400 years before the common era. He is often referred to as the father of modern medicine because he was one of the first to describe his medical observations in a scientific manner.

He is perhaps best known for his dictum expessed in Latin: *Primum non nocere* — or, "First, do no harm." It is part of the Hippocratic oath that is still attested to by medical school graduates.

Politicians should be administered a similar oath

when they take office. If they were, they might not have done all the questionable things we are dealing with in the current Covid-19 situation.

There is no doubt that Covid-19 is a virus dangerous to the elderly and the frail (and, early on, to those who live in New York City). But the fact is that the overall reaction to the virus has caused more harm than the virus itself.

As more and more data become available, it is clear that the resulting fatality rate from this virus will be around 0.2%. That is in the ballpark of a bad influenza season. It is also twenty times lower than originally assumed by the World Health Organization (WHO).

The fatality rate for Covid-19 residents of nursing homes and assisted living facilities account for close to 50% of all deaths in the United States; younger Americans have a much lower fatality rate from this disease.

In fact, the average age of Covid's fatal victims in most countries is more than 80. For Americans under the age of 25 there is a greater risk of being killed in an automobile accident than dying from Covid-19. Despite this, we have closed our schools and continue to cogitate about how and when to reopen them.

Moreover, the Covid-19 death toll itself is also now coming into question as the official figures do not differentiate death *from* Covid-19 versus death *with* Covid-19.

In addition, we are learning that many presumed Covid-19 deaths had no laboratory confirmation and may have been coded as such to capture increased reimbursement from various government agencies.

I believe that when the history books are written about this pandemic, they will show that our reaction to this virus was a great mistake. Worse, the continuation of our initial response to the virus is no longer just a mistake, it is bordering on malice.

With more than 30 million Americans unemployed at the height of the initial reaction to the spread of the disease and with estimates that 40% of those will not have jobs to return to, the economic devastation initially crippled America and the world. This self-inflicted economic wound has also caused an almost complete shutdown of the U.S. outpatient healthcare system.

Doctors from all over the country report devastating consequences to their patients. Recently I co-authored with Simone Gold, M.D., J.D., a letter to President Trump highlighting this aspect of the healthcare crisis. The letter can be viewed at *www.adoctoraday.com*.

Two days after the White House received this letter, Dr. Anthony Fauci of the President's Coronavirus Task Force changed his message to the public:

> *Stay-at-home orders intended to curb the spread of the coronavirus could cause "irreparable damage."*

A psychiatrist reported that his office volume is down by 80% and yet his prescriptions for benzodiazepines (Valium, Xanax, Ativan) are the highest in his career. Patients who require frequent visits to stay functional are not coming into his office for fear of contracting the virus.

A cardiologist reports that routine echocardiograms and other non-invasive cardiac testing protocols are not being administered because these procedures have been declared non-essential. Patients are afraid to visit a doctor's office.

A gastroenterologist reported that routine cancer screening colonoscopies have stopped altogether, and a gynecologist reported that cancer-screening pap smears and mammograms have ceased.

I am personally aware of

a 61-year-old patient who died of intestinal obstruction because he feared going into his doctor's office. Instead, he suffered at home, ultimately succumbing to sepsis.

These examples are being repeated across our country with devastating consequences. False information about waiting for a vaccination, the need for widespread testing, mask-wearing and potential asymptomatic spread of Covid-19 fill the airways and stoke unnecessary fear among the American citizenry.

Winston Churchill once noted that "Fear is a reaction, courage a decision." Maybe it is time for us to remember Dr. Hippocrates' statement from long ago: "First, do no harm."

It would go a long way to putting the current situation on the right track, not just by our doctors but by our elected officials as well.

IMMUNE
SYSTEMS
MATTER

PLANS AND DEMANDS for school reopenings are coming in fast and furious from government and nongovernment organizations alike. Some are hundreds of pages long, requiring a phalanx of Ph.D.s to sort through the details before implementation.

What seems universally clear is that no one is taking into account that the vast majority of us have immensely powerful immune systems that play a critical role in keeping us healthy and alive.

One plan calls for using sanitizing spray on all classroom surfaces multiple times per day; that children use hand sanitizer upon entering and exiting the classroom; and that all children and staff wear masks for the entire school day and, of course, practice social distancing. The bureaucrats at the CDC would be proud of the results.

But all of these "specialists" have ignored the fact that from the day we are born we are assaulted by germs — by the millions, if not billions. Our very existence is dependent on a robust immune system — that is, the ability of our bodies to fight off any invasion of bacteria, viruses, funguses, molds or other pathogens. Fortunately, we were created with a powerful internal standing army of cells ready to protect us in each battle and capable of winning most wars.

In order for our immune system to be prepared for those battles, it has to train regularly and bring new recruits to the effort. Even before we are born, our immune system is exposed to germs and is working to protect us.

The result is that our bodies create germ-specific special ops fighters to defeat a variety of enemies that life throws at us. Each time we are exposed to new or old germs, our immune systems grow smarter and stronger.

It is healthy and necessary for our very survival to be exposed to different germs and to recover to fight another day. If we purposely prevent such exposure, we may gain in the short term, but we may also lose in devastating ways in the long term.

You may remember seeing on TV an episode of *Seinfeld* titled "The Bubble Boy." In this 30-minute story a boy needed to live inside a plastic bubble because he did not have a functioning immune system. It didn't end well for the "Bubble Boy" when his germ-free bubble was violated and he was exposed to germs.

Modern society has gone overboard with deploying antibacterial soaps, lotions and cleaning products. They indiscriminately kill germs, yes, but they also wipe out the good bacteria that help maintain a strong and diverse microbiome. "Kills up to 99.9% of common germs," promises the label of one brand of hand sanitizer.

Everyone has a microbiome, a collection of more than 100 trillion (!) microbes that live on and in our bodies, the majority in our large (and clearly crowded) intestine. The more diverse your individual microbiome, the healthier you are.

Research indicates that early exposure to a variety of microbes may help lower the risk of developing conditions like asthma, allergies and even infectious diseases. Think of it this way: If you exercise regularly and your body is fit, you are less likely to be injured, be overweight, have cardiovascular disease or suffer from diabetes. When you stop exercising, your level of fitness declines, along with all the benefits.

Your immune system works in the same way: Stimulate it regularly, such as when a child plays in the dirt, and you are more likely to win the battles against dangerous germs and viruses, including Covid-19.

With Covid-19, we have gone "Bubble Boy" sterilization crazy, and it is not helping us. We now sanitize everything: bus seats, door handles, gas pumps, purchased products, our bodies.

We are cleaning our homes (and some offices) as if they were an extension of a hospital's ICU. I have one patient who told me he comes home from the market, takes off all of his clothes outside, hoses himself off, puts the clothes in a bag, and then takes a hot shower.

The fear of Covid-19 has driven us to sometimes ridiculous and unhealthful behavior.

SIZE MATTERS IN SCIENCE AND COMMON SENSE

CALIFORNIA'S GOVERNOR, GAVIN NEWSOM, recently issued an edict that everyone, with a few exceptions, must wear masks in public to protect against the spread of Covid-19.

A lively debate immediately ensued as to whether he had the authority to issue such an order. But what is more important, even if it is established that he has the authority, does mandating the wearing of masks make common sense? A large Danish clinical study of some 5000 participants in mid-November 2020 found that masks did not protect against the coronavirus.

Consider this: The virus particles associated with Covid-19 are about 0.12 of a micron in size. Why does size matter? Because the pores in a typical surgical mask can filter objects no smaller than 3.0 microns.

An N95 mask, if fitted properly to the individual wearer, can filter objects down to 0.1 to 0.3 of a micron. A 0.12 micron Covid-19 virus particle will pass through an ordinary surgical mask easily as well as any homemade cloth product. It is the equivalent of erecting a chain-link fence to keep out mosquitoes.

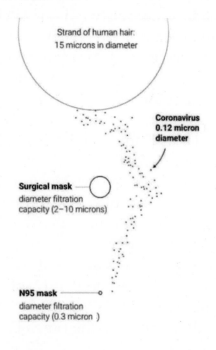

Strand of human hair:
15 microns in diameter

**Coronavirus
0.12 micron
diameter**

Surgical mask
diameter filtration
capacity (2–10 microns)

N95 mask
diameter filtration
capacity (0.3 micron)

There have been several studies about preventing the transmission of influenza and the common cold by wearing surgical masks. The studies concluded they were ineffective. That's why we are not told to wear them during flu season. There are no studies yet related to masks and Covid-19 — only anecdotal evidence that is mixed.

Fair enough, but a lot of readers will have heard that Covid-19 is mostly carried in droplets of mucus or spittle and any face covering will stop that. There is some truth to this. A sneeze or cough containing Covid-19 may be partially blocked by a mask or bandana. The science is inconclusive on the extent to which a sneeze or cough can get through these protective coverings.

But note this: As moisture builds up inside a face covering, its filtering ability drops precipitously.

Moreover, if Covid-19 virus particles are now trapped and building up inside a face covering, it could be re-infecting the mask wearer, going from the mouth into the nose. This does not even account for the fact that every time the mask is adjusted or touched the virus may be transferred to the wearer's fingers or hands and whatever is subsequently touched. And, please, never exercise in a mask — even a brisk walk in a mask can lower your oxygen saturation, cause headaches and put your health at risk.

Why then does a surgeon wear a mask during an operation? It is not to prevent a viral infection impacting the patient. It is to prevent the surgeons' and nurses' spittle, generrated while talking during surgery, from getting into an open wound and causing a nosocomial bacterial infection. It is also to prevent pieces of tissue splattering into the surgeons' and nurses' mouths.

If there were no need to talk during surgery, there would be little need to wear a mask — other than splattering tissue. Furthermore, a 2008 study of 53 surgeons by A. Beder showed reduced oxygenation and increased pulse rate after an hour of mask wearing during surgery.

But if I'm six feet away from another person, am I safe? There is zero science behind six feet of separation. The Europeans and Africans maintain a meter (about three feet) of separation. But why not four feet or eight feet? Because six feet was thought to be an easily remembered and calibrated number.

It is a guess that most people can't project the particles of a sneeze or cough farther than six feet. Common sense tells us that if you are not near an infected person you are less likely to get infected —

which is why it made no sense when the governor closed outdoor spaces such as parks and beaches. But since when have politicians been required to apply common sense?

Okay, back to size — the size of children! Little people are at very low risk of contracting Covid-19. In Orange County, California, we have had no deaths in children and only 20 deaths in the entire United States, all of which involved a serious pre-existing condition.

The CDC's website reports the risk of death in children from Covid-19 as 0.00%. Children have a 50 times higher risk of drowning and a much higher risk of being killed in an auto accident than dying from Covid-19. So why all the fuss about opening schools?

Fear is a powerful facilitator of public opinion, especially when it is in the hands of organized labor. Teachers' union demands are driving this narrative. The concern about school children wearing masks is that a child might be able to spread the virus to an at-risk teacher.

I have a patient who has Stage 4 breast cancer and is undergoing chemotherapy. This depletes her immune system, putting her at high risk of getting an opportunistic infection such as Covid-19.

We can either protect and if necessary isolate *her*, or we can mask everyone who lives near her or visits wherever she goes. Common sense tells us what to do. More important, we have multiple studies that show there is little evidence that children can asymptomatically transmit the virus.

The WHO indicated as such in June when Maria Van Kerkhove, M.D., the technical lead for the WHO's pandemic response unit, said: "... asymptomatic transmission appears to be very rare." Yes, political pressure caused her to walk back her comments the following day. The politics of health-care is getting ugly.

So what should we do? Mask up if you *feel* you must, but don't blame it on science. A school child should never wear a mask and socially distancing among children also makes no sense.

A healthy society protects the most vulnerable and isolates those who are sick. Covid-19 poses only influenza-like risk to the young and the healthy under 65 years of age.

We should size up this pandemic properly, ignore the sensation-mongering headlines, and act with a touch of old fashion common sense.

BETTER TO BE GOOD OR LUCKY?

AS EXPECTED BY most observers, the number of cases of Covid-19 continues to increase. There are primarily three reasons for the spike in cases:

1. More testing is being performed.
2. People are moving about as the economy opens up.
3. Massive protests and riots across the country.

The net statistic that will be used to frighten the American people will be the increase in hospitalizations that will follow the expanded number of cases. Days or weeks after hospitalizations grow in number, even more deaths are likely to arise.

What will not be reported in the gloomy news roundups is the fact that we now have effective treatments for Covid-19. More appalling, many doctors and hospital systems are refusing to use these effective therapeutics.

Dr. Vladimir Zelenko, a New York family medicine physician, has pioneered a treatment strategy that works well but is still shunned by most of the medical profession and ignored by the mainstream news media. Dr. Zelenko said this on Dennis Prager's radio show of July 10, 2020:

> I don't care what 'they' say anymore, I would rather speak directly to the American people and tell them I have some very good news for [them]. We have an answer to the terrible infection, we have a very effective way of treating it. In the high-risk groups there is a 99.3% survival [rate] and a 84% reduction in hospitalizations. There is also a 100% survival rate in low-risk patients when treatment is started in the first five days [after the onset of] an infection.

One of the key reasons for the increase in hospitalizations has also not been widely reported. The increase is in part due to the reopening of hospitals to elective surgeries and procedures. These had previously been categorized as non-essential by many state authorities.

Hospitals are also using ICU wards to isolate Covid-19 cases and not for the usual ICU acuity care. In addition, some of the ICU admissions are for relatively routine, not Covid-19, hospitalizations.

The early treatment of Covid-19 patients with mild symptoms has proven overwhelmingly effective. In Texas, Dr. Richard Bartlett has a 100% track record of no deaths with his treatment of Covid-19. As part of his protocol, he uses an inexpensive inhaled asthma steroid called budesonide. This treats the pulmonary inflammation that is often the culprit in the death of patients with Covid-19.

Both hydroxycholoquine and budesonide are only a fraction of the cost of Remdesivir, with its multiple thousands of dollars per dosage. Is there a financial incentive in maligning the cheaper treatment alternatives? One has to suspect that.

Dr. Zelenko's protocol of hydroxychloroquine + zinc + azithromycin has been made publicly toxic because President Trump mentioned just the first ingredient during a briefing on March 19, 2020. Yet a study released on July 2 by the Henry Ford Health Systems in Detroit showed a significant reduction in death among more than 2,500 hospitalized patients using the Zelenko cocktail of medicines.

For reasons that are not clear, the national media has refused to acknowledge this hydroxychloroquine study result, perhaps for fear that President Trump might be given some credit for promoting the drug. Information on the study can be found on the Internet under "Henry Ford Health study."

Chloroquine — a derivative of quinine, the extract of the bark of the cinchona tree — was developed in the 1930's as an alternative for the treatment and prevention of malaria. As most are aware, malaria is a mosquito-borne illness that has long been the scourge of the world's tropical regions.

Chloroquine was first used in a significant way during World War II in the Pacific Theatre. Later, soldiers in Vietnam were given weekly doses of chloroquine to prevent them from contracting malaria. All evidence points to its relative success in this usage with only 46 deaths out of more than 50,000 attributed cases.

Hydroxycloroquine is a better tolerated and more effective derivative of chloroquine, first approved for use in the United States in 1955. It has been part of the effort of medical science to find a more efective way to deal with malaria.

The generic version of hydroxycloroquine has been around for many years and costs only pennies per dose. Studies eventually demonstrated that the drug also showed promise for the treatment of other chronic illnesses like rheumatoid arthritis and systemic lupus. By now, its safety is unquestioned and it has even been approved by the FDA for use during pregnancy and breastfeeding.

So, if you are someone who has recently tested positive for the Covid-19 virus, there is great hope for you. The challenge is to find a doctor who is not overly wary of the political waves generated by the disease.

Among the newest medications is Regneron's REGN-COV2. This was one of the medications used to treat President Trump's Covid infection. REGN-COV2 is a combination of two monoclonal antibodies designed to bind to one of Covid-19's distinguishing spikes. This reduces the viral load and the clinical symptoms.

Compare REGN-COV2 to Remdesivir. It works by imitating a building block of the virus's RNA. Just as a defective Lego block prevents the expansion of a Lego structure, so a defective element of the virus's RNA stops it working properly. Add zinc. It disrupts the virus's replication mechanism to create a potent trifecta of medicines to help return those infected by Covid-19 to good health.

If you are not currently positive for Covid-19, there is a lot you can do to maximize your ability to block the infection from coming your way.

First and most important, take care of yourself by eating healthful food, exercising daily, maintaining your proper weight and taking an immune-enhancing supplement.

Check with your own physician prior to using any medication. Here is a list of the supplements I recommend to my patients to keep them from getting infected:

- Zinc — 25 mg daily
- Vitamin C — 3,000 mg daily
- Vitamin D3 — 5,000 IU daily
- Melatonin — 1-2 mg at bedtime
- Quercetin — 500 mg daily
- Fish oil — 3,000mg of EPA + DHA

In addition, stay well hydrated, avoid sugar and excessive alcohol. Get plenty of fresh air and sunshine, stress six to eight hours each night, and most important, manage your stress.

Should you contract Covid, work with a doctor who understands that effective treatments are available outside of a hospital setting.

NOT DYING IS BAD FOR HEADLINES — COVID-19 CASES VS. DEATH

AS WE TRAVEL the bumpy Covid-19 path back to normalcy, you would never know that we are headed in the right direction.

Teasers on television and headlines in newspapers report a "surge" in new cases of Covid-19 as well as hospitalizations; the

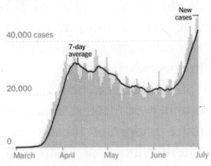

New reported cases by day in the United States

the teasers and headlines, of course, fail to mention that the most important measure of our progress in getting ahead of the virus is the number of *deaths* recorded. The fact that the rate of fatalities to infection is very low now is seldom if ever mentioned.

After weeks of unnecessarily shutting down our economy and the travesty of closing schools, it was certain that cases of Covid-19 would spike as we reopened society — *duh.*

When the massive protests and riots around the county over the succeeding weeks are taken into consideration, it ought to be no surprise that cases are increasing. It is important to remember that the purpose of "flattening the curve" was to delay cases and deaths from Covid-19 to a future date when our healthcare capacity was no longer threatened with being overwhelmed.

The great news is that the number of deaths, and perhaps more important the fatality rate (the likelihood of death from infection), have plummeted. Why? Because this virus tends to be very mild in the young and healthy — the cohort that has been most susceptible to infection of late.

The CDC data show that as of July 1, 2020, deaths among people younger than 25 are fewer than 170 out of a total of 120,000. It is almost non-pronounceable to state a fatality rate — too many zeros after the decimal point.

Covid-19 Deaths By Week They Occurred

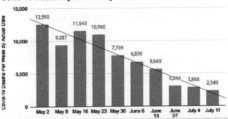

My point is this: If you are young and healthy, you have nothing to fear from the coronavirus except the fear-mongering from the media.

The average age of the "new cases" now spiking is 31 years old — similar to the age, by most estimates, of the protesters and rioters recently in the streets. I looked carefully at news coverage and videos of the protests and riots across the country and couldn't find many participants who looked 65 years old or older.

Moreover, I couldn't see much social distancing going on either! Yet, we are told that reopening restaurants, bars and retail stores — most of which had tried to arrange for social distancing and some of which required masks — is the source of the spike in new cases. I guess it was just a coincidence that approximately two weeks after the protests and riots an uptick in new cases was recorded.

But it is nothing to die for: The reason we continue to see a drop in deaths from Covid-19 is because a younger group is being exposed to the virus and we are much better at treating it.

Hydroxychloroquine + Z-pack + zinc have proven effective for early and mild infections. Doctors are also now using anti-inflammatory steroids (Dexamethasone and Prednisone) earlier and more aggressively in treatments.

The length of hospital stays for Covid-19 is also now dropping. Early on I wrote that the Covid-19 fatality rate will turn out to be in the ballpark of a bad influenza season. This is now becoming the case. The more we test, the lower the fatality rate as well. Approximately 98.6% of infected people will experience either no symptoms or mild symptoms and approximately 99.85% of all infected cases will recover.

Here are the most current CDC statistics on survivability of Covid-19 by age:

AGE RANGE	RATE
0-19	99.997%
20-49	99.980%
50-69	99.500%
70+	94.600%

A healthy society protects its most vulnerable members and isolates the sick while allowing the healthy individuals to go about their lives. Let's celebrate the drop in deaths and stop sensationalizing the "new cases" of Covid-19 as worthy of another shutdown.

SHE DIED ALONE

SHE WAS ALONE in her room in the nursing home. For the past two months she had been receiving hospice care for heart failure and a chronic lung disease. Several years before, her family had made the decision to transfer her to the nursing home as her health care needs became unmanageable for the family.

As a mother, grandmother and sister, she had plenty of visitors — often several times a week and always on Sunday. She seemed happy. The staff at the nursing home was very attentive and the facility itself was clean, comfortable, even homey.

Then Covid-19 hit in March and everything changed for this family: No visitations were allowed, no meals could be shared, no hugs or kisses permitted, no one to get closer than two arms' lengths away. The escalation from resident to hospice care occurred soon after the pandemic began lurking around the facility. The family believed her deterioration could be correlated to the withdrawal of human touch from her loved ones.

She passed away in May with no family at her bedside, no one to hold her hand, no friend or relative to whisper something lovingly in her ear. While she died peacefully, she left this world utterly alone. It didn't have to be this way.

The circumstances of this story have been repeated thousands of times across the country and the world. Almost 50% of all Covid-19 deaths in this country have occurred in nursing homes. Most deaths in nursing homes, however, are not *due* to Covid-19.

There are countless other causes of death. Yet all visitations have been banned for everyone in a U.S. nursing home. How does it make any sense to condemn an entire population of every nursing home in America to loneliness? Could such an edict do more harm than good?

Isolation is deadly — we have seen the highest suicide rates since the Great Depression. More children have died from suicide than Covid-19. The shutdown of houses of worship, schools and businesses has had devastating consequences. It may take us years to recover from this foolish decision.

Consider this:

- If we can fly crosscounty safely with masks on, why can't we be with a loved one during their final days utilizing the same precautions? We have rapid Covid-19 testing that provide results within an hour. Couldn't these be employed by nursing homes to ensure that visitors are negative for the coronavirus?
- If we can shop safely at Costco with masks on, why can't we worship at a church, synagogue or mosque just

as safely? Surely being able to pray is just as important as buying merchandise at a discount.

- If we can wait in line to buy a bottle of liquor or a six-pack of beer without danger, why can't we just as safely wait in line to vote on election day? Wouldn't all of us consider voting equally important to getting a buzz on?

- Why can't children attend school in person, but adults can attend a political rally if they like? Children are at very low risk for contracting Covid-19. Note that as of August 18, 2020, only one child under the age of 18 has died of Covid-19 in the state of California, whereas many more have died of influenza. We do not routinely close schools due to an outbreak of influenza, yet we are closing them all over the country because of the threat of this virus. Our children are unnecessarily suffering from being out of school. I wish the fact that child abuse reporting is down 25% were the result of a less violent world. Unfortunately, we aren't that lucky. We have more abuse but less reporting.

Looking at these instances, the conclusion is clear: Covid-19 is no longer a healthcare crisis; it is a crisis of the soul of America.

I hope you will join me in pointing out these realities and inconsistencies to our decision-makers. There is hope that a growing number of Americans are waking up to the reality that our American way of life is in jeopardy.

Like generations before us who waged war to protect America, we are being called upon to fight for the country we love now. Although we are not at war, our fight is equally important and difficult.

Fight by questioning everything. Fight by supporting candidates for local office (school board and city council) who understand what is at stake. Fight by running for office yourself. Fight by peacefully protesting. Fight by writing letters to the editor or posting on a social media site. Fight by being a little uncomfortable in speaking out. I am.

I cried writing this piece while thinking about the lady who died alone with no family members nearby. It is so very sad for those that are unnecessarily suffering. Join me in fighting to preserve liberty in our land.

Notes/Questions

DEFUND THE POLICE: WRONG TARGET, RIGHT IDEA

THE MANY CALLS to defund the nation's police forces make no sense at all — another slogan without definition, another emotional reaction without thought.

Yet, the idea of defunding government agencies that do not deliver the public services they promise makes a lot of sense. Underperforming government schools and their powerful unions would be a good place to start.

The failure of government-owned educational services in the United States is irrefutable. Study after study has shown that millions of American kids graduate below their grade level in math and ELA (English language arts). Embarrassingly, we spend more money on this type of schooling than almost any other country. Talk about value for money; we get none.

Let's get specific. I served as one of five elected members of the Los Alamitos Unified School District's Board of Trustees for 12 years. It was one of the top performing districts in Orange County, California.

During my time on the board, we routinely analyzed the results of California's annual required standardized tests, principally the California Assessment of Student Performance and Progress (CAASPP) in two basic categories: math and ELA. The 2018–19 results show that 48.9% of students were below grade level for ELA and 60.27% below grade level for math.

These results are even more depressing for students in minority communities. As you can see from the following graphs, there has been little change in student performance over time:

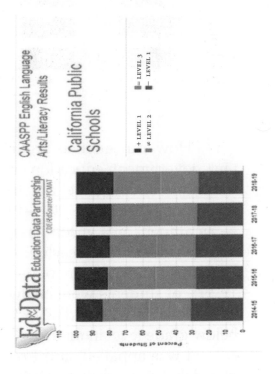

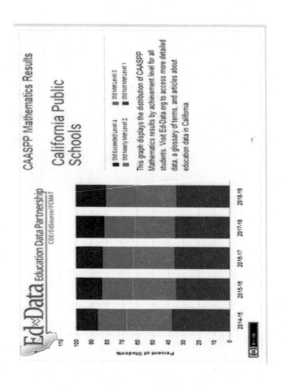

How can anyone argue that government education in California is doing the job? In my school district in 2018–19 — an affluent area encompassing the cities of Seal Beach, Los Alamitos and Rossmoor — 19.35% of students were below grade level in ELA and 42.67% below grade level in math.

I was appalled, and I realized that to argue that only inner-city schools are underperforming is a fallacy. When I first saw our abysmal math scores, I offered three recommendations that were summarily rejected by the school district's professional administrators and even by my fellow board members.

1. The first proposal I made was to make participation in elective activities, such as athletic teams and performing arts programs, contingent on achieving grade level scores on standardized tests. We would provide extra help and tutoring for students as needed. I was told we could not do this — it would be viewed as discriminatory by other students, teachers and coaches. I was also told the teachers' union would never allow this, as it could impact teacher employment. Furthermore, I was told that if not for these elective activi-

ties, some students would simply drop out of school. I argued that this would encourage better academics and put elective activities in perspective.

2. My second recommendation was to provide a financial incentive to teachers to increase student achievement. I was told this would not be legal because teacher compensation is a negotiated item with the union and our "Uniform Compensation System" is a law that must be followed. Under the law, teacher compensation is based solely on years of employment and educational achievements — never on competency. In an era where we are re-examining police policies dictated by police unions (keeping disciplinary records hidden from the public, for example), we should be

re-examining this job protection provision as well.

3. My final recommendation was for the district to provide vouchers to every student who is below grade level. These could be used with a private tutor or with one of our own teachers offering tutoring services. I was told that we could not do this because it would imply that our own teachers are not capable of teaching our own students, and it would cause undesired pushback from the union. Let's not be unnecessarily disruptive, I was told.

Los Alamitos High School math scores continue to be abysmal right along with those from the rest of California and the country. I doubt that parents even realize that this failure is occurring. We keep doing the same thing over and over yet expect different results — the best definition of insanity we have, whether Albert Einstein said it or not.

Those on the political left are correct about defunding — they just need to redirect their defunding energies to deserving government targets.

RIOTING MUST NOT BE ALLOWED TO DEFINE A NEW AMERICA

EMBEDDED IN THE fabric of America's freedoms is the right of the people to "peacefully assemble" and to "petition the Government for a redress of grievances."

Nothing in the Constitution, however, gives anyone the right to riot, loot and burn down any part of any city. Yet in some cities across America, there seems to be an assumption of an unwritten right to do just that.

Our founders correctly believed that all men are created equal, that they are endowed by their Creator with certain unalienable rights, and that among these are life, liberty and the pursuit of happiness.

The rights of George Floyd, the Minneapolis black resident who was slain by the police in 2020, were snuffed out. The officer who was responsible for this act is now awaiting a murder trial along with those who stood silently by.

Justice is underway. Its wheels may turn slowly, but an old saying has it that they grind exceedingly fine. That requires us to have patience and trust in an imperfect system that by all accounts is considered one of the best in the world. It is a system that can be changed by a deliberative process undertaken by duly empowered government representatives. It is not designed for the emotional tantrums of an out-of-control, radical mob.

At no time is our civil society more at risk than when lawlessness is encouraged and allowed to overtake our justice system. "No justice, no peace" is an often heard rallying cry of those protesting in the streets.

Except whose justice is in question and by what measure is peace achieved?

The constant drumbeat from those on the political left holds that America is endemically racist, that our "systemic and institutional" racism has been harmful to any progress or healing.

"Repeat a lie often enough, and it becomes the truth" is an axiom of propaganda often attributed to the Nazis' Joseph Goebbels. As I look at it, The New York Times 1619 Project is an example of this type of propaganda.

I have been a volunteer reserve deputy for a local law enforcement agency for many years. I was recently deployed as a tactical medic for a SWAT team to help with local protests/riots. In my many years involved in law enforcement, I have never seen "systemic or institutional" racism.

Our SWAT team is mult-ethnic and multi-racial.

I have never viewed my team members through any lens other than competency. I read a recent opinion piece where the author stated:

> *A majority of white Americans still cannot come to terms with what black people have known forever: Racism is systemic, systematic and nowhere near gone.*

There are many black conservatives who differ, and we had a two-term black president who got the majority white vote overwhelmingly.

There are bad apples in every profession and every walk of life. It is the nature of human existence. We must not confuse the few with the majority. We must not allow peaceful and righteous protesters to be overtaken by radical groups that use the cover of an unjust act to further their own socio-political agenda.

Peaceful protesters and

politicians must speak out loudly against this anarchy. Where is justice and where is peace for those store-owners whose establishments are looted and torched? Where is justice and where is peace for the innocent bystanders who are injured or killed? Where is justice and where is peace for injured or killed law enforcement officers taking a stand to protect innocent life and property? Where is the outcry when a church in Washington, D.C., built in the 1800s is torched?

The path forward must include an intolerance of lawless acts of violence and looting. We must use the full extent of local law enforcement, bolstered as necessary by the National Guard, to shut down the riots immediately and return civility to the streets.

Martin Luther King Jr. once said:

> *The limitation of riots, moral questions aside, is that they cannot win and their partici-*

pants know it. Hence, rioting is not revolutionary but reactionary because it invites defeat. It involves an emotional catharsis, but it must be followed by a sense of futility.

That futility must be followed by an open dialogue where feelings are discussed but facts drive policy. Racial division is a useful tool for those who want a radical progressive change to our government institutions. Saul Alinsky, the author and political theorist, knew this well when he stated:

The despair is there; now it's up to us to go in and rub raw the sores of discontent.

Those who came after America's founders had a different vision for America. They believed protecting "one nation under God, with liberty and justice for all."

I hope most Americans today feel the same.

BLACK LIVES MATTER IS NOT WHAT YOU THINK

AS A SWORN reserve deputy for a major sheriff's department, I cringe with disgust whenever I see any unjust police action. During my academy training, we were required to memorize the California Law Enforcement Code of Ethics. Here is the first paragraph:

> *As a law enforcement officer, my fundamental duty is to serve mankind — to safeguard lives and property, to protect the innocent against deception, the weak against oppression or intimidation, and the peaceful against violence or disorder, and to respect the Constitutional rights of all men to liberty, equality and justice.*

Unjust police actions impact the authority of every sworn officer and hurts the reputation of every law enforcement agency. This is why it is vital for law enforcement representatives to speak out against the bad apples anywhere in the justice system — not unlike how it is done in the medical field.

The Black Live Matters movement is really two disparate groups. One identifies with the idea that black people have been unfairly treated by society. These BLM supporters often wear the T-shirts, carry the signs, chant the slogans, and demand political and economic change. These supporters are not part of the second group, which is a formal organization that maintains a website advocates revolutionary goals, seeks large amounts of money and is controlled by radical leadership.

The first group of adherents to the BLM message is larger and likely not aware of the extremist organization whose water they carry; the second group is smaller, more disciplined and raises some fundamental issues that need close examination. I refer to the first group as "BLM Supporters" and the second group as "BLM Activists."

In reading BLM's website and listening to interviews of BLM's co-founders, I realized that it was not born of the unrest of 2020. It was founded in 2013 following the death of Trayvon Martin. As a reminder of this seminal incident, Martin was a 17-year-old black high school student visiting relatives in Sanford, Florida. George Zimmerman, a bi-racial neighborhood watchman with a weapons permit, shot Mr. Martin after an altercation between the two. Zimmerman pleaded self-defense under Florida's "stand your ground" law and was acquitted.

As the original movement grew, it failed to pay attention to factors that have caused many of the race-related problems the country has confronted. The destruction of the black nuclear family and missing black fathers, for instance, are arguably the single most detrimental societal change America has witnessed over the past 100 years. Out of wedlock births is a corollary. Worse, these changes have too often been incentivized by government policies.

Every weekend in major inner-city neighborhoods the death toll from black-on-black murders is staggering. Black lives do not seem to matter to the BLM organization under these circumstances. The young perpetrators are more often than not from fatherless homes. BLM activists are not only silent on this issue, they seem to advocate for this new family construct on their website:

> *We disrupt the Western-prescribed nuclear family structure requirement . . .*

Hanging on the wall in the Orange County Sheriff's training academy is a quote from Dr. Martin Luther King, Jr. I make a mental note to read it every time I am at the academy:

> *Injustice anywhere is a threat to justice everywhere.*

MLK taught us that we should judge others not on the basis of the color of their skin but on the content of their character. BLM activists say something different: "We work vigorously for freedom and justice for Black people . . ." In law enforcement, we are sworn to protect the freedom and justice for *all* people equally.

Sometimes law enforcement tragically misses the mark (as do all professions), but we shouldn't destroy or defund the whole law enforcement structure because of a few rogue incidents. We should deal with them. Bad cops should be fired just as bad teachers should be removed. Nobody hates bad cops more than good cops.

Lady Justice is always portrayed with a blindfold; the idea that justice — from cop to court — is applied without regard to wealth, power or status. Should we raise the blindfold in certain instances so she can peek out with an eye toward taking better care of black Americans? BLM Activists, I suspect, would say yes.

There is another critical factor that differentiates BLM Activists from BLM Supporters. The co-founders of the BLM movement are unapologetically Marxist – followers of Karl Marx, the revolutionary German philosopher whose ideas have inspired the governments of all the communist regimes.

BLM co-founder Patrisse Cullors explicitly said that she and fellow BLM co-founder Alicia Garza are "trained Marxists." On the BLM website they state: "Our members organize and build local power to intervene in violence inflicted on Black communities . . ."

The Los Angeles Chapter of BLM held a rally on June 23, 2020. The message: "We are demanding that the

School Board vote . . . to defund school police by 90% over the next three years." This theme is often endorsed by political leaders on the left.

It is time we no longer embrace the slogans of BLM Supporters or the radical agenda of BLM Activists.

Instead we ought to embrace and stand for the American way of life, characterized by a color blind society, adherence to the tenets of the U.S. Constitution, and a return to traditional American family values.

Thomas Jefferson is credited with saying that "Eternal vigilance is the price of liberty." We must be vigilant — or we may very well lose the country the vast majority of us of all faiths and colors and creeds love.

IT'S JUST
A TEST

I HEARD THIS startling story from a patient the other day: "I got a phone call . . . telling me my Covid-19 test came back positive. But I never had the test done, I told the caller. I checked in and completed the paperwork but I left because the wait was too long. They never [actually] tested me."

Incredibly, the caller didn't believe my patient. "No," she insisted, "I am sorry . . . your test results were positive." Worse, I suspect that these bogus "results" were sent to the state data bank that reports "new cases" to the CDC. One more error in the Johns Hopkins numbers that most of the media rely on.

I have read numerous other accounts similar to this on social media. They never seemed credible until several of my own patients reported directly to me that this is exactly what happened to them. Then, a member of my office staff reported the same experience.

Concerns about the accuracy of the multitude of Covid-19 tests being used are commonplace and with good reason. But now, the issue of ghost tests calls into further question the validity of the whole testing process itself.

Why would Covid-19 results be fabricated? Is it a simple clerical error? Are financial incentives being given for increased testing productivity? Are politics at play — the more tests administered, the better the bureaucrats in charge look?

But here's the important thing: If we can't get the basics right and if the numbers are wrong, how can we expect the experts to make the best possible public policy decisions for the country? We can't, and we can end up doing things that are actually inimical to the well-being of the people of this country!

Another real life story: One of my patients owns a business in the city of Long Beach, California. An employee of his, with whom he had direct contact, tested positive for Covid-19. As a result, he decided to get himself tested. So, he drove to a Covid-19 testing center.

The Sofia rapid nasal test was used at this site. This testing system uses an immunofluorescence-based assay. To my patient's consternation, he, too, tested positive. All of a sudden, he faced a cascade of unpleasant but necessary decisions including the cancellation of a long anticipated golf trip to Bandon Dunes, Oregon.

The next day he took his wife to the same testing center; he also decided to re-test himself just to be sure. Naturally, both he and his wife tested negative for the virus this time.

So which of the tests is correct, he wanted to know? Both my patient and his spouse had no symptoms. We are taught in medical school to treat the patient, not results of tests. So, no treatment was instituted. But I wanted to know whether my patient's positive test from the day before had been reported?

Many of my patients that test positive go back and retest — sometimes multiple times until they get a negative result that conforms with how they feel. They do this for a variety of reasons: Legitimate concern about being contagious, mixed with paranoia; return to work policies of their employers; and lack of confidence in any single test, to name a few.

If a patient were to test positive three times over a couple weeks, is every one of those positive tests sent to a central data bank? Could this be in part why we have seen the number of cases escalate? More positive tests lead to more multiple testing of a single patient. What if I test positive while on a trip to a different state and then test positive when I come home? Are my results counted twice with each state registering each new case? If the basic data begins to be suspect, how can you trust the effectiveness of the public policy on which it is based?

A recent Journal of the American Medical Association research article in *JAMA Pediatrics* indicated that children could be spreaders of the virus as they have a higher viral load when tested.

"Our analyses suggest children younger than 5 years with mild to moderate COVID19 [sic] have high amounts of SARS-CoV-2 viral RNA in their nasopharynx compared with older children and adults."

More fake news? What the *JAMA* article failed to tell

readers is that the Covid-19 test the researchers used was the new Abbott Laboratory test that is not FDA-approved to provide quantitative data. That test is approved for qualitative data only.

In other words, the Abbott test is meant to answer whether there is virus present, not to determine how *much* virus is present. Scroll down to the end of the *JAMA* article and note what you see: Harsh criticism from physicians and Ph.Ds who call the findings reported in the article misleading at best and fraudulent at worst.

The author of the report is William Muller, M.D., Ph.D. He is on the staff of the Ann & Robert H. Lurie Children's Hospital of Chicago, a part of Northwestern University's Feinberg School of Medicine. He responded to the outpouring of criticism this way: "We very much appreciate the attention this paper has received and the comments left by different readers. Several readers have left comments on technical characteristics of the assay used to generate the reported data. While it is correct that the clinical application of the assay is for qualitative detection of SARS-CoV-2 RNA, the cycle threshold data reported in this study were gathered for research purposes."

Fine. But what does all that mean? The mainstream media ran pieces about this article and never saw the criticism calling the conclusions patently false.

It should not be forgotten that just a short time before this episode, two of the leading medical journals in the world, *The New England Journal of Medicine* and *The Lancet*, both within hours of each other, retracted separate research articles that were critical of hydroxychloroquine

It is no wonder that so many people have lost faith in

our so-called healthcare experts and seem hopelessly confused as to what is to be believed about the dangers to their kids, their parents and themselves.

When the basics are wrong, how can anyone trust that the larger public policy decisions are right?

FEAR FATIGUE

Our daily lives are filled with risks, lots of risks. Just look at these examples:

- Every year 30,000 to 40,000 Americans die in automobile accidents, yet none of us is willing to give up cars to avoid the possibility of dying in a car crash.
- Heart disease kills more than 600,000 of our fellow citizens annually, yet we continue to eat fast food and pack on extra pounds.
- Diabetes helps kill more than 80,000 Americans a year, yet sugar is still part of the food supply.
- Suicide takes the lives of close to 50,000 Americans annually, yet we have instituted Covid-19 policies that have increased the in-

cidence of suicide to the highest levels seen since the Great Depression.

- Millions of children are infected with influenza each year and hundreds die from the disease. But we have never closed our schools or insisted on masking the population to try to prevent the spread of flu.

- Child abuse and child sex trafficking are at record levels and many specialists believe that it is due, in part, because our schools are closed while adults are unable to go to their normal places of work.

The CDC estimated that as many as 500,000 people died worldwide from the H1N1 virus in 2009 — the first year the virus circulated. Overall, 80% of H1N1 virus-related deaths were thought to have occurred in people younger than 65 years of age. Despite this, we didn't close the schools, mask the population, or shut down the economy.

In 1968, the Hong Kong flu killed approximately four million people globally. Our economy remained open in the face of those staggering numbers; moreover, the three-day Woodstock festival in upstate New York rocked on during the epidemic.

Isn't it time we stopped living our lives and dictating what we can and cannot do based on fear of every new danger? Instead, shouldn't we let each individual decide what risks he or she is willing to take?

The famous declaration in President Franklin D. Roosevelt's first inaugural address seems as apropos today as it was in 1933:

The only thing we have to fear is fear itself.

We are Americans —
the freest, most prosperous
society in the history of the
world. We fought to end
slavery, losing over 600,000
people in the Civil War. We
have fought in two world
wars and played a dominant
role in winning both. Those
wars cost the lives of more
than 500,000 Americans.

We take risks to enjoy
the freedom they gave us —
or at least we used to. We
ride motorcycles, skydive,
climb mountains, and drive
too fast. We eat the wrong
foods, drink too much alcohol, and live in ways that are
often not healthful; but, we
cherish our right to do so.

"Better Safe than Sor-
ry" has NOT been elevated
to a national motto. It doesn't
appear on any flags; no one
is rushing to buy T-shirts em-
blazoned with those words.
But, "Live Free or Die"?
That's a different story. It is

the motto of the state of New Hampshire and was a colonial rallying cry. The words " ... and the home of the brave" end the national anthem. Do we still believe it is?

Fear is far deadlier and more contagious than Covid-19. Fear raises our blood pressure to unhealthful levels; fear influences us to make poor decisions. We fear being criticized, we fear exposing our ideas, we fear offending others, and we fear being infected by a virus that is not much more deadly than viruses of the past.

As a physician with more than 25 years in practice, I will tell you what I tell my patients: You should not fear Covid-19. You should properly prepare and protect the most vulnerable in your homes, your businesses and in society; but you should join everyone else in living your life in maximum liberty with common sense protections and precautions.

We have an effective treatment when symptoms of Covid-19 are seen early and remain mild. These treatments can also offer protection for the most vulnerable.

Stop listening to those that want you to stay in a state of chronic fear. Turn off the mainstream media constantly using fear to capture your attention. Don't let those who want power over our lives to gain more of a foothold in Washington.

Turn on friendships and optimism and life. Turn on church and community and hope. Live with purpose, and fear fatigue will never become a problem.

COVID-19 VACCINATION — WARP SPEED AHEAD

A vaccination against Covid-19 has now been approved and is available to designated groups.

This will be the quickest scientists have ever been able to develop a new vaccination for a major disease. It typically takes years to create a new vaccine, but sometimes despite the best efforts of scientists, success eludes them. As a result, we have no vaccination against HIV, hepatitis-c or malaria, to name just three examples.

The technology used

for the first Covid-19 vaccinations being brought to market by Pfizer and Moderna uses an mRNA or messenger RNA technique. The Covid-19 virus is an RNA virus, meaning that the genetic code is carried in the virus's ribonucleic acid or RNA.

> Messenger RNA is the instruction manual that cells use to manufacture proteins. An mRNA vaccine instructs human cells to manufacture a specific Covid-like protein. This protein, once formed, then stimulates our immune system to produce an antibody to fight against this Covid-19-like protein. The antibody is ready, then, to attack the real virus should it be introduced into our bodies.

Significantly, this is the first time that an mRNA mechanism is being used in a vaccine. For the most part, mRNA technology is used in cancer therapy. It has had some success in producing various proteins to attack and disrupt certain cancer cells. Most of the commentary so far suggests that it may not be too much of a leap to use this approach in vaccines as well.

The vaccine developed by AstraZeneca for Covid-19 uses a different mechanism. It takes an adenovirus that has been modified to include genetic material from the SARS-CoV-2 virus so that it introduces the immune system to the spike protein of the Covid-19 virus. The immune system then produces antibodies against the spike protein.

The good news is the AstraZeneca vaccine can be

stored at normal refrigerator temperatures for up to six months. The bad news is it is only about 70 percent effective. This vaccine, however, may become the preferred one in third-world countries because of the storage issues.

Is there controversy connected with the use of these new vaccines? Yes. Here are some of the areas of concern:

- The trial data on the vaccinations released so far have not addressed the issue of transmission of the virus. That is, the efficacy data are based only on symptoms and Covid-19 testing, not on transmission. Could the vaccine create asymptomatic carriers who can unknowingly transmit the virus?
- Most other previous

efforts to develop vaccines have used animal studies first to assure safety in humans. This was not done with these new Covid-19 vaccines.

- One of the possible complications from the rushed development of these vaccines is something called immune enhancement. One type of immune enhancement is known as Antibody Dependent Enhancement (ADE).

- ADE is a process in which a virus leverages antibodies to aid infection. In short, the Covid antibodies, stimulated by a vaccine, could amplify the infection rather than prevent it. This paradoxical reaction has been seen in other vaccines and animal trials. Only through extensive testing can this effect be identified and prevented.

This has not been done with the approved vaccines and, if the ADE effect is present, it might not become apparent until months after the vaccine has been administered to populations around the world.

- We are told by the vaccine manufacturing companies that the efficacy of the Covid-19 vaccination — based on their clinical trials — is in the 90 to 95 percent range. A vaccine that protects all but 5 percent of those vaccinated is very impressive — if these numbers hold up as the vaccine receives wide distribution in the population.

- The efficacy of a controlled study, however, may be very different from the experience in the real world when massive numbers of people are involved.

For example, data from the Centers for Disease Control and Prevention show that the influenza vaccination efficacy for the 2017-18 season was approximately 38 percent; only 20 percent was achieved in the 2018-19 season; and just 39 percent for the 2019-20 season.

When the influenza vaccination was first introduced in 1938, the efficacy was expected to be much higher than current numbers suggest.

- Assume, for the moment, that the efficacy of the first Covid-19 vaccines is indeed in the 90 percent range. The CDC data show that the survival rate of those contracting the disease goes up as age goes down. If you are less than 70 years old — 99.5 percent; if you are less than 50 years old — 99.98 percent; and if you are under 20 years old, the chance of surviving Covid-19 is 99.997 percent.
- For the record, seasonal influenza is a greater risk to the young than is Covid-19. Weighing the benefits versus the risks of accepting the Covid-19 vaccine could be very difficult, especially for the young. It

is unlikely, therefore, that I will recommend vaccinations for my young patients to protect them against a virus that more than 99 percent of them would survive should they contract it. For young people, Covid-19 is far less dangerous than influenza. However, my final recommendation will also consider emerging data on the potential lingering long-term effects of post-Covid-19 infection — so-called "Long Covid" symptoms.

- The same companies (and executives) that look to profit from this vaccine are also immune from all liability. In 1986, Congress passed the National Childhood Vaccine Injury Act (NCVIA).

It provides immunity from liability to all vaccine manufacturing companies. Many people are working to change this law. Rather than blanket immunity, I would propose establishing national *limits* to damages along the lines of California's Medical Injury Compensation Reform Act (MICRA).

- Will enough people get the vaccination to help reduce the spread of Covid-19? At best, only 50 percent of us choose to get an annual influenza vaccination despite the fact that it is widely available, inexpensive and safe. In 2018 only 45 percent of those older than 18 received the flu vaccination. In 2017 that number was

37 percent. Even for seniors older than 60 this number reaches only 68 percent.

- We know that blacks have been disproportionately affected by Covid-19. Should they and other minority groups be given preference for the early allotments of vaccinations? If they are given a preferential position to receive the vaccine, will they take it?

- Minorities tend to be skeptical of the government and especially vaccinations administered by the U.S. Public Health Service. The USPHS and the CDC carried out 40 years of secret experiments in a study of syphilis, using blacks as test subjects. Can we overcome such a history to get the vaccine to the most vulnerable?

- We know very little about the longevity of the immunity acquired for Covid-19 from natural infections or from the vaccines. Will the vaccinations give long-lasting immunity or will a booster be needed? Recent studies have shown that the body's immune response to the virus — as measured in levels of antibodies and T-cells — tends to wane over time. We have no lasting immunity from influenza, for example. Since the virus is constantly mutating, we have to get a new flu shot annually.
- The detailed safety data for the vaccines

have not been released as of this writing. Are two months of trials enough time to be certain of the safety of the vaccines now being presented to the public? What about *long-term* safety ramifications?

- Without these data, I am against a mandate to force this vaccination on anyone. In light of the limited safety data, it must be a voluntary prevention strategy.
- In 1976 we attempted a mass vaccination of the population with a newly created swine flu vaccine. The vaccination program was aborted, however, after some 450 people came down with Guillain-Barré syndrome, a rare neurological

disorder. How will the memory of this epic government failure affect the rollout of a new mass vaccination program?

- We are now hearing rumblings that the Covid-19 vaccination could be made mandatory for air travel, international border crossings or other activities such as entering a theme park or government building. What could possibly go wrong with that requirement?

I am not opposed to vaccinations, per se, including the Covid-19 vaccination. I am very hopeful that the vaccines will be safe and effective for those at highest risk.

But I am opposed to any government requirement for the vaccination or any private or public dictate about the vaccine that infringes on a citizen's freedom of choice. I strongly support informed consent for all vaccinations, which currently is not the U.S. standard. I am, however, opposed to the immunity granted to pharmaceutical companies by the provisions of the NCVIA.

Moreover, there are still many unanswered questions about the Covid-19 vaccination.

- Who will be eligible to receive the limited quantities when each batch becomes available?
- How will the long-term safety of the vaccinations be monitored and assured?
- How will the logistics of the distribution be handled closest to the consumer for any

vaccine that requires sub-zero transport and storage?

While these questions are being answered and the other caveats mentioned above are resolved, we have to note that we are getting better and better at *treating* Covid-19: the death rate in terms of population continues to fall, hospital stays for Covid-19 get shorter, and hospital mortality from Covid-19 plummets.

A Covid-19 vaccine, in other words, should be viewed as one of many tools to combat the pandemic but not as the savior that many believe has arrived.

ABOUT THE AUTHOR

Dr. Jeffrey I. Barke is a board-certified primary care physician who has a concierge practice based  in Newport Beach, California.

He completed his medical school training and family practice residency at the University of California Irvine and earned his undergraduate degree at the University of Southern California.

During his more than 20 years as a physician, he has served as an associate clinical professor at the University of California Irvine's Medical School, chairman of the Family Medicine Department at Hoag Memorial Hospital, on the board of directors of the Orange County Medical Association and medical director of Pathways to Independence.

Dr. Barke was elected to three four-year terms as a member

of the Los Alamitos Unified School District Board of Education and is currently an elected member of the board of directors of the Roosmoor Community Services District. Dr. Barke is a co-founder and current board chair of Orange County Classical Academy, a free public charter school in Orange, California. Dr. Barke also serves as a reserve deputy and tactical physician for an Orange County law enforcement agency.

Dr. Barke co-authored *The Essential Diet Planning Kit* (with Godfrey Harris) in 2005. He has appeared multiple times on the *Dennis Prager Show*, the *Larry Elder Show* and on *Fox News Special Report* with Bret Baier.

He is married to his high school sweetheart, Mari Barke, who is currently the vice president of the Orange County Board of Education. They have two adult children, both of whom live out of state.

ACKNOWLEDGMENTS

I wish to thank my wife of over 30 years, **Mari Barke,** for her support, ideas and tolerance of my new social media activities. She is also the photographer who made the head shot of me that appears with my biography.

My daughter, **Allie Barke**, played an important role in helping with social media and creative content. She also designed our logo (shown at the end of this section) and maintains my website:

www.rxforliberty.com

Thank you also to my son, **Sam Barke**, for pushing me to stay in the fight with courage. Special appreciation goes to my business partner, **Dr. Kenneth Cheng**, for allowing my passion to flourish and to the staff of **Personal Care Physicians** of Newport Beach, California, for fielding calls to the office — not all of which are supportive!

I am grateful to **Dennis Prager** and **Larry Elder** for inviting me to share my views on their radio shows and for writing the book's Foreword (Prager) and saying those nice words on the book's back cover (Elder).

After the first edition was published, **Kirk Cameron** said this: "In a news-cycle when propaganda is more common than truth, Dr. Barke gives us researched medical facts and common sense about COVID-19 to help us thrive in the midst of an unprecedented national panic-demic." **Pastor Rob McCoy** of Godspeak Calvary Chapel, wrote: "The facts and truth contained in [Dr. Barke's book] have served to empower people to overcome fear and stand against tyranny of those who would use lies to take our freedom. His courage and wisdom have been a great blessing to me personally as well as those I serve." I am moved by these words and appreciate them deeply.

I was taught that there is no such thing as good writing, only good rewriting, so thank you to **Godfrey Harris** and **The Americas Group**'s stable of specialists, especially editor **Art Detman,** without whose help this book would not be possible.

Thank you also to the *American Thinker* (www.americanthinker.com) for publishing most of these essays. Special appreciation to **Earick Ward** for co-authoring some of the pieces in the book and supporting my efforts to give our ideas a wider audience.

I must also acknowledge the work and contribution of **Simone Gold**, M.D., J.D., founder of America's Frontline Doctors. I am proud to be a member of this courageous organization empowering patients and physicians with independent, evidence-based medicine.

Finally, it has been quite a bumpy ride for the United States over the past several months. I have tried to put forward a common sense approach to dealing with Covid-19 issues and the societal upheaval that was in part spawned by the pandemic.

I have been called a hero by some and a quack by others — my home county is fractured by vehemently held opposing views like never before. The coming weeks leading up to the Presidential election will likely be filled with more turmoil.

I will continue to write and speak as time permits and express my thoughts on social media. I have been humbled to have been given an opportunity to have my voice heard across America and carried into foreign lands.

I am hopeful God will bless me with continued energy, strength and wisdom to lead with facts and science and help America.

I am looking forward to feedback from readers in the hopes of improving my message to better communicate common sense to close the widening gap between healthcare and politics.

Dr. Barke's blog can be accessed at
RxForLiberty.com

INDEX